Contents

MIGRATING MINDS II

Migrating Minds II

A collection of poetry & prose

by
Bayside Writers

Migrating Minds II
First Published in 2006 by
MS Publishing
Mid-Sutton Community Centre
Dublin 13.
ISBN NO 0 - 9548438-1-9

Thanks to all the primary and secondary schools
for their valuable contribution and all the new lights that have
added to our latest collection.

The Publisher acknowledges financial
assistance from Fingal County Council

Fingal County Council
Comhairle Contae Fhine Gall

Design & Layout: Conor O'Malley
Front cover photo (*Irelands Eye*): ©Copyright Conor O'Malley

Printed by **Colour Books Ltd**
Baldoyle Industrial estate, Dublin 13

PREFACE

It is a pleasure to introduce Migrating Minds II, a collection of poems and stories by mainly local writers.

On this occasion it is an honour to have on board our sailing craft, young people from Bayside Primary School, Gaelscoil na Camógie Clondalkin and secondary students of Pobailscoil Neasain, Baldoyle, The Donahies and St.Finians, Swords. I thank the teachers for their cooperation and support.

A special thanks also to the poets who live in the neighbouring parish Baldoyle, and who again generously share their poems with us.

The people in our writing group come from a variety of backgrounds, and as in our first collection, we continue the themes of scattering and gathering like the coming and going of winter birds to the estuary. Reflecting this constant movement we include poems and stories which loosely reflect a theme of 'Homing'.

Sadly, over the summer one of our members, Joe Fitzpatrick passed away. He shared with us his love of poetry, and we miss his lively contributions at our meetings. We are proud to include his writings in this collection.

I also thank the members of Bayside Writers for their friendship and help in making the poems and stories for this book. Though we live in a parish in our writings, we strive to keep in mind Patrick Kavanagh's concluding lines from his poem *Epic*:

" Till Homers' ghost came whispering to my mind he said:
 I made the Iliad from such
 A local row. Gods make their own importance".

I know you will enjoy the diverse imaginations of writers spanning the generations in this collection.

Paddy Glavin

My First Word

My mammy picked me up
And put me on her knee,
I made a little noise,
And then she smiled at me.

She called out for my granny
And she came running in,
My mam said I said something
So I made the noise again.

And now I'm all grown up
But my mam is still the same,
She's still going on about
That little noise I made.

Ann Marie Barry
Bayside Primary School

Colours of the Year

Spring is yellow with bits of green,
and cherry blossoms on the trees.

Summer has bits of yellow and blue
with ice-cream parlours and beaches too.

Autumn is a golden brown and red,
and leaves go swirling around my head.

Winter is streaks of white and silver,
Christmas is coming and people shiver.

Spring, Summer, Autumn, Winter,
those are the seasons of the year.

Finbarr Daly
Bayside Primary School

Different Times in Life

Christmas time, Easter time
Winter time, Summer time
Home time, school time
Communion time.

Birthday time, quiet time
Play time, work time
Family time, friend time
Confirmation time.

Now I'm ten
I've nearly done
All of them.
Time is flying
By too fast.
So whenever you
Have spare time
Do what you like
BEST!

Emma Runswick
6th class -Bayside Primary School

Future

The future is like a paper aeroplane,
You don't know what route it will take,
You can suffer much pain,
You might not wake.

The future is a bunch of twists and turns,
Like a country road in winter.
Your boss might be a Mr. Burns,
You might end up in a dumpster.

The future has not happened,
The future is a different place,
With five born every second,
Colonies in outer space.

Is future just a fate?
A split second on a road,
Family planning, funeral date
Killed because in a car he/she rode.

Anon

School Day

Early in the morning, I get up out of bed,
The sun shines through the window far beyond my
head,
Down to put the kettle on, a cup of tea for me,
Pop a slice in the toaster, toast soon to be!

School-bus arrives at the door and off to school I go,
I run fast in the yard and join the end of the row,
I do well in school, the best I possibly can,
If the heat is bad the teacher will turn on the fan!

When home time comes and dinner is ready,
I'll be so hungry, my hands won't be steady,
After supper it will be time to sleep,
Before my dreams I'll be counting sheep!

Mark Breheny
6th class-Bayside Primary School

The Fifth Day

If only I had a few more years,
I really only had two.
I would have seen her beautiful face,
I would have seen her lovely eyes look up at me,
I would have played with her all day,
I would have laughed at all her jokes.

But that could never be for
Five days she was alive,
And on the fifth day she died
So that was her life that came to an end.
And that is how I never had a sister,
But still she might look down on me.

Colm McGoldrick
5th class-Bayside Primary School

Time to Write a Poem

"Time to write a poem" teacher says.
Everyone groans and shakes their heads.
"Long or short it can be
But do it quick and quietly".

Oh no. I can't write a poem
I'd be better going home.
Oh dear I'm running out of time
I can't make anything rhyme.

I could write about my school
Or even the swimming pool
I could write ancient Rome,
Oh look I've already got a poem!

Eimear O'Keeffe
6th class-Bayside Primary School

Time

Time is a big thing
Like propeller jet wings
Time is a big fuss
Like waiting for a late bus
Time goes so slow
If you do not show
Time goes fast
If you've had a good past.

Kevin McQuaid
4th class-Bayside Primary School

Time!!

There are many different times
In life, some bad, some good,
Some with strife. Mine is fun
I have to say, My favourite
Time is when we play.

When the clock strikes ten, its
Time for bed, that's what mum
And dad have said. So here I
Am now playing with my toys
'cause tomorrow they'll all be broken by the boys!

Anon

Time II

Time is a baby growing fast
A film and its cast,
Time can be quite a lot of things,
Autumn, Summer, Winter and Spring.

All this time can mean quite a lot,
But remember use it wisely.

Don't waste it, throw it or give it away
But don't keep it and hide it for another day.

The last thing I have to say is time is
Precious and is not here to stay.

Louise Keogh
5th class-Bayside Primary School

What is time ?

A clock ticking and tocking
A night sky at night
All the stars out at night
The whole day gone.

The Summer ahead
All Spring gone
The Autumn ahead
All Summer gone.

I stayed up late last night
The early morning sky
The dusk evening sky
The pitch black sky at night.

The Winter ahead
All Autumn gone
The Spring ahead
All Winter gone.

Time goes fast
Time goes slow
Well the clock ticking and tocking
The whole year is gone and bye for now.

Andrew Cluskey
6th class-Bayside Primary School

When I was younger...

When I was younger
Like when I was one
I would always have lots of fun.

When I was two,
If someone said something disgusting
I'd always say "ooh".

When I was three
I called my babysitter "Bose"
Even though her real name was Rose.

When I was four
I ripped up a teddy
Whose name was "Little Freddy".

When I was five
I began school.
I started to dive into the swimming pool.

When I was six
I hated my school uniform
I had to wear it every term.

When I was seven
I got my first bike
That was something I really liked.

When I was eight
I went to France
And I did a funny dance.

Fiona Carroll
4th class-Bayside Primary School

How to Learn From Dandelions

Splotch of sun, poured from a cup,
scraggy hairy tangy rough...pure promise...
never give in, never give up.
Walking, people step on you, but it's all right;
you spring back after the foot has gone. And guess what?
A child knows you cast her unspoken longing for an answer
when she blows into the wind your puffball
and maybe when you remind me of Christ Child
glopping fingerpaints on the grass, He is telling me
something worth holding to. Life is its own answer;
hang on, like a dandelion, part weed, pure
full of sunlight, just the same. Silent
when you roar your colour, you have the still
full quiet, and the intense beauty which
is what life gives when you hold it, like a cup.
We leave you growing still, or cast your
seeds into the air to settle.
And this will always be.
Dandelion, dandelion, sing silently to me.

Sue Brown

Sometimes members of the poetry group work with children in primary school. I was in Gaelscoil na Camógie, Clondalkin, and the children and I had been talking about animals. We were imagining being at Creation, helping God think up so many wonderful animals. They all contributed to making these poems together.

God took

the soft white mounds of snow
and the shyness of deer
the silent watching of moon
but ripples like wind over grass
the warmth of a pink beating heart
and he made RABBIT.

God took

the roar of a waterfall
but wrapped it round
in soft gold cloth,
He draped it with fine-spun gold straw
and then He hung an old rope for a tail
but it was a gold rope.
He made LION.

And God took

warm golden sand and shaped it
tall, shy and awkward, suffusing it
with gentle browsing curiosity
and His Child splashed yellow blobs
from His bucket of sunlight
and They made GIRAFFE.

Last,

an old brown sack full of bones,
a wise and sometimes irritable uncle
to other animals, but a soft heart
beating, and a love of branched antlery trees
old like him...
God loves MOOSE

School Days

The alarm bell rings
Three times, no more
Toes search for slippers
Find them
Vision blurred
Looking for blue
I wrestle with the garment
Until it contains me.
Cereal clangs
In the porcelain bowl.
Spoon, food mouth
Like clockwork
Enter school
Cocoa, marshmallows and all
Warms the soul.
Registration,
Very simple
Call 'here!' when you hear your name.
Work to do
Homework to get
Plenty.

Robert Long
St. Finian's Community College
Swords

Exams!

Biting nails,
Grinding teeth,
Twitching eyes,
Shuffling feet.

Last minute nerves,
Time to start,
First exam's
History of Art.

Monet, Manet,
Or something like that,
I'm getting mixed up,
And I don't like that.

Now I'm snapping,
Starting to freak,
Dying to run out,
And just start to shriek.

Wait, what's he saying under his frown?
Oh no it's time,
Pen's down,
Time to go and all over again I pick up a fail, oh and my
pen.

Paul Behan
St. Finian's Community College
Swords

MY JOURNEY THROUGH THE UNDERWORLD

Footsteps break the silence. I'm drawn to a young couple strolling happily through the puddles of rainwater. As they pass the man stops, and digs five Euros from his pocket, adding that *anyone who is out on a night like this must be bad.* I thank him and ask him if he has the time.

"Two a.m. and may God help you", he replies.

Damn I had missed the 'Salvation Armies' soup delivery again. I was starving now. I spend my days playing the guitar hoping for the price of a can of cider. I guard my meagre possessions at night. I walk the back lanes in search of leftovers at the rear of restaurants.

Ah! there's a bin just left outside "The Indian Palace" complete with congealing "Tikka Masala" and bright pink prawns.

I look around in case anyone is watching. Plunging my hand into the grimy depths I pull out several cartons of food, and sprint down a side alley. I run and run until my legs feel exhausted. The city is quiet now save for the barking of dogs that the noise of my footsteps disturbed.

I sit on the damp cobbles and take out my pickings. I horse into the chicken chow. I realize now why it was in the bin. I fling it from me. I'm not that desperate.

"Excuse me Sir, if you don't need that food I'll have it",

A voice comes from a filthy lane.

A figure emerges from the shadows and gripping my guitar I'm ready to bolt.

"There's no need to worry", the figure reassures me.

"I'm desperate for a meal".

I focus on the mysterious figure.

In front of me is a female, about fifteen or sixteen, around five feet nine with wild blue eyes and a mane of shocking red hair.

I hand her some food and she devours it. Though it is dark with no moonlight I notice her blushing. She attempts to return the leftovers but I refuse. I recall the words of the man I met earlier, *Anyone who is out on a night like this must be bad.*

She is wearing a baggy green tunic that makes her look even

thinner then she is.Sticking two mangy fingers in her mouth she whistles into the night.

Sounds of breathlessness precede the arrival of two, no three young children.

She hands the leftovers to them. They devour the lot in seconds.She whispers 'a thank you'.

I know I must help her.

As she shoos the children away I search the pockets of my torn denim jacket until I find the five Euros. As she faces me I take her hand and place the note in it.

Gasping she shakes her head and is going to run away. But when she looks in my eyes she knows I'm ok.

She kisses me on the lips and with her children runs away into the night.

I sit and strum the twelve bar blues and think that for the sake of five Euros and one hungry night I had met my first love.

Orla Gilleaney
Donahies Community College

What Would?

What would you say
If I said I loved you babe?
Would you go
Or would you stay?

What would you do
If I left it up to you,
Would you kiss me
Or would you go?

Go down where the dusty Angles go,
Go down where the thirsty grass won't grow.

A fly on the wall
Makes you feel so small,
As you sit on the floor
Where he left you.

A tiger's eye
A glistering brown,
As you sit there
And watch your life go down.

Go down where the dusty Angles go,
Go down where the thirsty grass won't grow.

Go down, Go down, Go down
Go down, Go down we'll go down.

David Yates (Jr.)
St. Nessan's Community College.

A Thought for Tomorrow

This will be the year
The best one to remember,
From January till December,
12 months of mayhem,
7 days of bliss,
Welcome to the new world,
Welcome to heaven,
Welcome to hell,
Walk up to the gates,
And ring the bell,
Entertainment tonight,
There's a VIP in sight,
All the successors,
And all the kings men,
The actors and the models,
Singers and dancers,
They all wait frantically,
With the shepherds and sheep,
How deep the thought of tomorrow,
And if it will ever end,
A question for the Gods,
An answer for the pope
To give some hope,

For the congregation,
And the village of dopes.

Daniel Kelly

THE LITTLE COMET *Cathal Melinn*

The galaxy was bright blue black, twinkling and purple misty in places one Tuesday evening. On this Tuesday, a little traveller, a pretty little comet, who was after having her lunch in the Milky Way, zipped through the sky to visit her friend Portia.

Portia was a stage actress and a big one too-she was a real star. She was older than the Little Comet but always threw some light on the path she should take. Portia had a really warm heart in her centre and always gave the Little Comet pointers on what she should do in her life.

Portia and the Little Comet had been good friends ever since Portia found her going in circles around the place where her family used to live. Many moons ago, the poor little comet got lost from her family one day while she was on a roundtrip with her parents and two brothers.

They had taken the galaxy highway but had gone too fast near a danger black spot. They had been travelling for two hours and had taken the wrong turn past the Mars Bar and Restaurant. The whole family ended up on the dark side of the moon and in the panic, the Little Comet had gotten lost.

It had been nine years since she had seen her parents and brother, but she never gave up hope. Each and every day she would look around the places they used to go together, just in case they came back but they never did.

As it had been some years since she had seen her parents, she was afraid that they wouldn't recognise her and her brothers might have forgotten about her, for they were younger than her. Her friend Portia always helped with her bright sparkling wisdom on life and the Little Comet loved her for this.

Now she was a pretty little comet and although she was older, she tried to look the same so her family would recognise her. So every morning, when she woke up, she would tie her long golden hair back in a tail that would trail behind her whenever she went fast.

Well she had been playing ring-a-rosy with Portia that Tuesday evening and had gotten a bit dizzy because she really went too fast. Portia didn't mind and she laughed when the Little Comet said that she saw stars.

After spending most of the evening with Portia, the Little Comet went on her merry way. Unfortunately she had forgotten her umbrella and got caught out in a meteor shower. Now the Little Comet's hair was dull and her ponytail was all flat.

She took shelter near a friendly moon and tried to dry her hair with the sun when suddenly, four comets who looked like her family zoomed past. The Little Comet looked up and recognised her father but they didn't recognise her with her dull flat ponytail. She called to them as loud as she could but they didn't hear her. She called again but they were going so fast that they were soon but a glimmer in the distance.

The Little Comet was very sad because she missed her family and her spirits had been dampened by the meteor shower. She began to cry and cry and couldn't stop.

All of her friends were very sad for her; they had never ever seen her like this. Luckily, Portia who was wise and fair knew that her family would come back. The Little Comet believed her and was happy again.

In the meantime, her father, mother and the two boys were heartbroken. They had searched the four corners of the universe for the Little Comet, whom they all loved, but she couldn't be found.

Her mother asked her friend the White Dwarf who was so old and wise that his hair was very white and he had gotten smaller every year, but he didn't know where she was.

"Maybe she passed by but I'm so small I can't see past the cosmic mist," said the White Dwarf. The Little Comet's mother said "thank you and goodbye" to the White Dwarf and he promised to keep an eye out for the Little Comet.

Her father asked the Red Giant, whom everyone feared because of his size and fierce temper, but he let a roar so loud that the heavens shook for he did not like to be disturbed. So her poor father had to go back to his family with no good news about Little Comet's whereabouts.

At this time, her brothers took it upon themselves to ask the asteroids who would play down at the video arcade but they didn't know her although they agreed to keep watching the skies in case she should pass.

All the while the Little Comet grew sadder and sadder for she had seen her family and they didn't even recognise her.

"Maybe they don't love me anymore," she sobbed as she passed a big black hole on the galaxy highway.

"What's the matter ?" said a voice from the hole. "It's so dark in here, I never know what's the matter. Is there someone out there?"

"I'm here, the Little Comet, I've lost my family again and I'm very upset," cried the Little Comet.

"Come closer and we can talk," said the strange voice.

The Little Comet was a bit scared in case she fell into the hole - her parents always told her never to talk to a stranger. But she was so upset that she forgot what her parents told her and slowly she went towards the hole. As she got closer she felt herself slip further and further until she couldn't stop herself. She was falling into the hole!

"Help me! Help me!" she screamed but she was in space and no one could hear her voice. Suddenly the voice from the hole started laughing louder and louder.

The Little Comet stumbled back and back but couldn't help falling further and further into the hole.

"What's the matter, Litttle Comet? No one knows anything about matters in here," laughed the voice.

The Little Comet screamed her loudest and was getting closer and closer when, in a flash, she was saved by none other than that inter-galactic hero — the Supernova.

The Supernova carried her away from all the dangers in the black hole and dropped her safely off overlooking the sea of tranquillity. She felt the power of the space waves when the Supernova shot off to help a moon who had dropped his trousers.

A few days had passed before this little traveller found her way back to Portia and the rest of the stars. She told them about the black hole and the brave Supernova. Portia understood that the Little Comet was young and told her in a nice way that she must be careful, especially around strangers. The Little Comet said that she was sorry and wouldn't do it again.

On the other side of the universe her family heard word of their daughter, the black hole and the heroic Supernova and began to make their way towards this famous scene.

On their way they saw a sign for a play called "The Merchant of Venus" in which Portia was a star. Her family had never met Portia, only the Little Comet knew her since she had gotten lost all those years ago. It had been many moons since the last time the family did something together so they decided to see this much talked about play starring Portia.

The crowds gathered for the cosmic ballet before the main performance; and everyone took their place and the show began. The Little Comet had been given a special seat in the balcony as she was a close friend of Portia. Her parents and brothers sat watching the play on the far aisle below the Little Comet's balcony but they never saw each other.

Half way through the show, the Little Comet spied her father leaving for the bathroom.

"It's them, I can see them, look," she said. "Ssshhh, my mother's speaking," said Portia's sun.

"But look, I've got to get to see them," whispered the Little Comet.

"Ssshhh'" he repeated. The boy who was young and shy, locked the balcony so they couldn't get out and he could see his mother acting in the play. Oh the Little Comet tried and tried but couldn't leave.

When the show was over and everyone began to go home, the Little Comet sped down to where her parents were but they were gone. The crowds had gotten in her way and she was on her own again.

She wandered aimlessly around after the show, for she was very sad. Well she was about half way home when she bumped into none other than her youngest brother. They were so happy to see each other that they spun and sang and danced through the night sky, but after a little while her brother began to cry.

"What's the matter? Are you sad to see me?" she asked.

"No, no but now I'm lost," he said

This broke her heart for her brother was very young and she loved him dearly. She told him about Portia and how she would help them both and he grew happier. So the two made their way back to Portia and her friends.

It took about twenty minutes to get home and as they arrived they saw a crowd talking to Portia who was giving out autographs. The two little comets sped up. They went faster and faster until they got right up to Portia. They stopped for a minute and just then, their father stepped out from behind the biggest star in the galaxy. The Little Comet and her brother were overjoyed and raced to greet him. The closer they got the more excited they grew. Just then, their mother and brother stepped out too. All of them. The whole family, together again.

"How did you know where to find us?" cried the Little Comet, holding back tears of joy.

"We were talking after the show and your brother went missing," said her father.

"We were really upset," said her mother, "but Portia said she knew of a little comet that had lost her family."

"That was me," cried the Little Comet.

"And now we've found you both," sobbed her mother, "we've found you my most beautiful little girl."

Portia took a moment. She looked over at the family now back together and she smiled. Although she was a famous star, she never lost her love for helping others. She then looked over at her own sun and grew warm with love inside. Portia was a very special star and was filled with joy when the family agreed to stay close by so they could all be together. And everyone took care of each other and there would be no more getting lost from that day onwards.

Linski's Graduation

As the gown of distinction flows
Like a mythological cloak, it speaks in volumes of silence.
Its colours denote an ancient house of learning,
Four hundred years whisper in corridors of a distant past.
Voices from another time seep from walls of knowledge,
One can feel the swish of a million gowns of distinction.

As that distinctive breeze meanders, percolates in its own time
A young lady moves in a royal cortege.
That perfume of achievement scintillates the brimming senses,
A day which once seemed so far away is now a reality.
Time spent trying to circumvent books of learning
Has now brought that ship of dreams to its harbour.

With pride parents levitate in rapture
As they watch a young woman, once a child
Glide majestically on a sea of joyous tears.
As those tears flow freely memories speak in gentle tones.
The mood of the day creates a warm tropical feeling,
Graduation, is the culmination of dedication.

Thomas Delaney

Return to mildness

At the equinox of Spring
Comes the stormy weather of change
But now St Patrick is past
Winter is past
And Easter Peace is near
March gives way to April-May
Cold, wind, rain turn to sun and showers
Breezes westerly
Waking to the softer mornings
And the evenings getting longer
Refreshingly
All is brightening
Gradually
Gladly birds are singing their hearts out
Christ is rising again
Again
Come then, my love, my lovely one,
Come

Paul Wickham

Dublin Sky

Chinese,
Watching Cranes in flight
See writing in the sky
Mystic messages in beak and claw configurations.

Brent Geese, in full flight across today's sky
Scroll into the sun
Uninterpreted.

Ann Colgan

Ha Haiku

Curtain back, wipe smudge;
Fellow staring smirks and nods.
Not waving!! Cleaning.

Eddie Phillips

Mum at eighty-eight

One slim lady hurray
Is two fat ladies today

Eddie Phillips

ALL FOR IRELAND *Emmet Vincent*

About a year ago I was in a rather dingy looking pub, that shall remain nameless, situated right in the city centre of Dublin. As the night was drawing to a close the DJ, in order to finish off his set with a bang, decided to play 'Amhrán na bhFiann'; our national anthem. Almost everybody immediately rose to their feet, hand on hearts and pretended they knew more words than merely the first and last lines. I'm no more knowledgeable either but I took the decision to opt out of the farcical charade and remained seated whilst our dreary, national anthem sounded out. Unfortunately, my lack of patriotism was spotted by a burly, beer-bellied, gorilla with copious tattoos of the Ireland flag and Celtic crest smothering his tree-trunk arms. He wasn't in the slightest bit pleased with my behaviour and accosted me for not loving my country enough to get up off my lethargic arse.

"Stand up now or I'll burst ya!" I think were the exact words he furiously uttered, to which I bravely retorted, "No problem Sir", before I reluctantly stood and began singing the words incorrectly at the very peak of my vocal powers. In my whole, entire life I've never been too fond of physical confrontations due to my phobia of pain. Perhaps if I had been of the fighting variety I could have argued with him and talked tough, saying things like, "I hold no affection for our national anthem for various reasons that you're probably too brain dead to understand but if you wish to step outside and discuss the matter further then I'd be delighted to accommodate your request. However, I must warn you that you will end up being quite sore." But I'm not the fighting type and I never will be, which could well be the reason why I loathe and detest 'Amhrán na bhFiann', translated into English as the 'The Soldiers Song.'

One thing I am nonetheless, is an avid letter writer. Not long after that unsavoury incident, I wrote to our Taoiseach, Mr. Patrick Bartholomew Ahern or Bertie as he likes to be called and asked him if he would consider changing our national anthem from the bleak 'Amhrán na bhFiann' to something more cheerful and uplifting. This is what I wrote in my first letter to him:

Dear Mr. Ahern,

Thanks for taking the time to read this as I know you're a busy man what with having to run the country and all that lark (you're doing a super duper job by the way). I am writing to request that you replace 'Amhrán na bhFiann' our existing national anthem, with something more melodic, less depressing and dare I say something that has absolutely nothing to do with war and all that silly nonsense. Maybe we could take a song that has already been written, perhaps by The Beatles. They always had nice, positive, catchy songs about love, walruses and all sorts of other fantastic stuff like that. Of course the decision is yours seeing as you're Mr. Taoiseach and I'm not. I'm just throwing these ideas out there. It's up to you to grab hold of them and put them into action. I hope this letter finds you well and congratulations on the Celtic Tiger. It's great.

Yours sincerely

Emmet Vincent

I hope you believe me when I tell you that Mr. Ahern wrote back. Sure it took a few weeks but eventually a letter from him came my way. He thanked me for my kind words and for taking such a keen interest in our country's national anthem. However, he didn't deem it possible to change it to anything by The Beatles as they hailed from England, not Ireland. He also pointed out that the costs would be astronomical to attain the rights for any of their music. The letter ended with him signifying his agreement that the Celtic Tiger was indeed great. My reply was as follows:

Dear Mr. Ahern,

Thanks a million for writing back. I've written numerous letters to Martin Cullen, Minister for Transport and not once have I received a response from him. I wonder why. He can't be that busy seeing that he's not even the Taoiseach. Anyway I digress. Using a Beatles song for our national anthem was just a suggestion. I myself don't feel that there would be any problem because of their nationality. Both Paul McCartney and John Lennon have Irish ancestry. Having said that, you're probably correct about the large amount of money it would cost in order to get the rights (no wonder you got to be Minister for Finance for three years). But all is not lost good Sir! How about we use a song by an Irish band or solo artist. They'd be obliged to give us the rights for free or at least at a discount. I'm a big fan of My Bloody Valentine. Two of the band members, Kevin Shields and Colm O'Ciosoig, are Irish. I must admit that their music wouldn't fall under the classification of catchy pop but that's a good thing in my opinion. If we did use a My Bloody Valentine song then we would certainly have the most original and interesting national anthem in the world (at least that I'm aware of). It would be heaps better than 'God Save The Queen' which is pretty much on a par with 'Amhrán na bhFiann' as far as melody and lyrics go so have a think about that. Anyway don't be a Martin Cullen and please write back A.S.A.P.

Yours sincerely

Emmet Vincent

It took longer this time for Mr. Ahern's second letter to be delivered to me. He pointed out the various obstacles we might face from the general public if we used a song by any artists be they contemporary or otherwise. He stated that music is very much a matter of individual taste and although there may be plenty of fans of My Bloody Valentine in Ireland, you can guarantee that there is also plenty who dislike them and it wouldn't be fair on those people. He seemed slightly more curt in manner than he had been in his previous letter. With great haste I wrote back:

Dear Mr. Ahern,

Thanks again for replying but I find your response less than adequate and steeped in negativity Fair enough I can see where you're coming from with regards to using a song that has already been written but that doesn't mean we should admit defeat. The Bertie I know doesn't give up that easy. So how about we write a brand new song? I'm not that adept musically but I could give it a go if you like. You could always get professionals to fix it up afterwards and I'd have no qualms about relinquishing creative control. What we need is a subject, that Irish people have a strong affinity towards, for the theme. I recommend tea. Do you know that the Irish drink more tea per head than any other nation in the world? Now what makes more sense Mr. Ahern? Having a national anthem named 'The Soldiers Song' when we are a neutral country or having a national anthem with a title along the lines of 'Tea! Mmmmm it's good' when our nation has such a passion for the tasty, soothing drink? I'll leave you to mull over my proposal.

Yours sincerely

Emmet Vincent

Months I waited until eventually I got another letter from our tardy Taoiseach. All he basically said was that he loved our national anthem and under no circumstances was he going to change it to anything written about tea and composed by a lunatic. My answer to this was:

Dear Mr. Difficult,

Why didn't you say that you had no intention of getting rid of our national anthem in the first place? I feel that both my time and money have been wasted. As a courtesy I would appreciate it if you reimbursed me for what I spent on stamps during this whole debacle. It amounts to 96 cents (I'm not billing you for the money I spent on the first stamp so count yourself lucky).

Yours,
Emmet Vincent

I'm still waiting for my money back and for the time being it looks as though I'll have to put up with our national anthem the way it is.
A few weeks back I was drinking in that dingy looking pub yet again and sure enough 'Amhrán na bhFiann' was played at the end of the night. I noticed the same frightening, burly chap, singing it fervently and scanning around him for anyone engaging in acts that could be construed as unpatriotic. I ducked behind a pillar so he couldn't see me and hidden from his sight, I gazed at the tattoos on his arms. He must really love this county I thought,

for after all, he was willing to put himself through the intense pain of having needles pierce his skin just so his arms would be green, white and orange. All for Ireland! His singing of the national anthem, albeit tuneless, was filled with emotion. All for Ireland! When we left the pub I witnessed him smash a glass bottle on the ground. All for Ireland! Then he took out his manhood for everyone to see and urinated right in the middle of the street. All for Ireland! As I hung around for a taxi I saw him litter the street with the remnants of a chip bag before threatening an innocent passer by. All for Ireland! Had he left the pub having just participated in singing about a certain tasty, hot beverage then it's possible he might have acted differently. Who knows?

THE END

Am I Right or am I Right?

I try to tell the truth
By telling a bigger truth
But reality shifts from day to day.
Each morning we yawn
As the radio retails the same story.
How can each night bear such atrocities?
They take the people from the street
And shoot them in a dark country lane;
Smearing the meadowsweet
With the screaming blood of the slain.
We stolidly dress for work.
Relieved that we did not know them,
Or the agents who slaughter in our name.
Am I right or am I right?

John Walsh

Buddleia

In October weather
On Howth Head
I stole a wild cutting
alongside purple heather.

I planted the faded shoot
in chill dark soil.
Now time has dressed the tree
in a green cloak

that thrives for a while,
and then fades until spring.
How can a life transplanted
take root and blossom?

Maybe a glimpse of light on the horizon
or a graft skilfully slit releases the sap.
It is summer now in the garden
The tree is laden with purple flowers.

Honeybees circle around.

Paddy Glavin

Sunflowers

Sunflowers are disappointing
I liked them better before they thrust
Their giant heads and gangly limbs
Into my life. In poems they sound
Golden and splendid, cousins of those girls
Who queened it in the dance-hall.
In my garden they're much too unkempt
To play at flower girls.
Van Gogh caught them in carpet slippers,
Broken-leaved, hair askew,
Spilling their sagging petals
At his feet.

Today the one my daughter grew
Is toppling out of the slim vase
Upsetting me with intimations of glory
In her sad seed eyes

Máiríde Woods

For a Real Friend

You are the warmth of a waiting room
the fire in the hearth as twilight blue
swirls in a frosty autumn afternoon.

Opening, the free blue sky soars
and leaves crackle like brown kindling's sparks —
and you — freedom and love mingle in your eyes
so warm and true — a welcoming free love is you.

Many shared hours live here now;
like the flames in the fire —
they settle us to talk, share life;

the travels told, the meetings kept
bless this hour and renew
the unspoken lively promise
between me and you.

Sue Brown

Rainforest

Karunda —
　　Cable car
　　　　Rain pouring in
　　　　　　Green and wet.

Looking down
　　Water
　　　　Above —
　　　　　　nothing.

No Light anywhere
　　Searching, reaching out.
　　　　Finding another lost soul.

Light within missing...

Her Brother gone on also.
Near Kevin's Bed, Glendalough.

John O 'Malley

Milés Milés
(Milés milés is the Latin name for The Badger)

Darkness fills my life
The night is my day
In Earth's womb I dwell
In fear
Of man

With hounds you come
To hunt me
In quiet den
With hound pack frenzy
Bloodthirsty man

I love the darkness
You the light
I hunt for food
You hunt for blood

Me Milés Milés
Lover of darkness
You Homo sapiens
Lover of slaughter

John Haughton

The Latvian National Anthem

Someone said something somewhere
Something not too loud from within the silent crowd;
Then a sound was heard, a dull thud of skull cracking.
As a crowbar smashed open a head
Blood, bone and brain flew through the air.
A madman with his shirtsleeves rolled up swung the bar again.
Once more one more fell and felt a second blow.
So on it went till all were gone to ground;
Then the sound of music, played by a man
who danced across the bodies.
Freedom filled the air; the Jews were dead at last!
Years have passed and yet that scene of sickening hate
Must haunt the souls that stood
without a word at such a sight to see;
Yet what would one like me do if I had been there too
To smell the blood and feel the fear that filled the air
For when madness makes men's minds murder
Few are found to voice the opposite view
And for those that do, hang in the air from every post and tree;
Some scenery to see, that stops the thoughts of sane men
And sends them home to close their hearts and doors
To thank their God that it's not them or theirs
That felt the blow of crowbar steel upon their skull;
And while their blood was still warm, were danced upon
To the sound of someone singing
The Latvian National Anthem.

Ken Bryan

EYE TO EYE CONTACT WITH BILL *Frances Glavin*

To hell with cataracts I muttered to myself as I left the eye specialist's rooms in Fitzwilliam Street. I'm going to see Bill. It was ten thirty a.m. on the fourth of September nineteen ninety-eight and the President of the United States was in town. I graced Woods of Baggot Street for morning coffee, and then hopefully set off down Merrion square. The police were much in evidence. I found myself thinking of an alibi for my presence in the area. My imagination had put on roller skates. I was innocent. I had no intention of harming the President. There would be no point in frisking me.

I came back to the real world as I saw some people walk rapidly towards Mount Street and form a thin line across the road. There was much banter as I joined them. "He won't even look at you," said one attractive girl to her friend, "You're no Monica Lewinsky". The sirens had started and the outriders came by and eventually a limousine bedecked with two flags appeared. We waved hopefully as they approached but we instinctively knew it wasn't the real thing. Then there was Bill, and I went forward with the others waving and shouting "Hooray". He waved back and looked at me. I swear that our eyes made brief contact. Well, if a cat can look at a president, a president can look at a cat, especially a Kilkenny cat!

That's my second President I thought. I had waylaid J.F.K. down near the Four Courts the night he came to Dublin. I had walked all the way from Terenure but he looked over my head. You never know with Presidents!

I stopped counting Presidents and made progress towards Pearse Station. Policemen canted out of cars. It got to the stage when I wanted to wallop a lamppost with my umbrella to see if it yelped. There was a book-barrow outside Westland Row Church so, of course, I bought a book, which the young lady in charge put into a brown paper bag. The significance of a brown paper parcel in a high security area escaped me at the time. A young man earnestly mouthed prayers in the back of the church. Could have been FBI or Special Branch or a refugee from modern living, I mused.

At the station I asked for a ticket to Raheny but I proceeded to the southbound platform, as I needed to visit the Ladies. The usual man wasn't at the barrier. He must have failed the fitness test for security. As I put my parcel on the wash basin a person came into the Ladies. She was tall dark and wore a smart denim trouser suit, and left without washing her hands and, wait for it, didn't look in the mirror. I was writing the film script in my head at this stage.

I went through the tunnel to the northbound platform and looked across at three railway workers dressed in impossibly clean reflective jackets. One was talking on his mobile and another had a rucksack on his back. I wonder what clean railway workers carry in rucksacks? There was another walking down the line apparently checking out sleepers. I opened the brown paper parcel!

There were really normal people in my carriage, and the hairs on the back of my neck resumed their usual position. There was a man with his little girl. He complained that she wouldn't stop talking to strangers. I refrained from advising him to put her towards a career in R.T.E.! When I landed on the platform at Raheny there was a railway worker in a slightly smudged reflective jacket talking to people and actually laughing. I felt like hugging him. As I walked home I paraphrased the popular song - My mama never done told me there'd be days like this!

Death of a Field

The field itself is lost the morning it becomes a site
When the Notice goes up: Fingal County Council — 44 houses

The memory of the field is lost with the loss of its herbs

Though the woodpigeons in the willow
And the finches in what's left of the hawthorn hedge
And the wagtail in the elder
Sing on their hungry summer song

The magpies sound like flying castanets

And the memory of the field disappears with its flora:
Who can know the yearning of yarrow
Or the plight of the scarlet pimpernel
Whose true colour is orange?

And the end of the field is the end of the hidey holes
Where first smokes, first tokes, first gropes
Were had to the scentless mayweed

The end of the field as we know it is the start of the estate
The site to be planted with houses each two or three bedroom
Nest of sorrow and chemical, cargo of joy

The end of dandelion is the start of Flash
The end of dock is the start of Pledge
The end of primrose is the start of Brillo
The end of thistle is the start of Bounce
The end of sloe is the start of Oxyaction
The end of herb robert is the start of Brasso
The end of eyebright is the start of Fairy

Who among us is able to number the end of grasses
To number the losses of each seeding head?

               I'll walk out out once
Barefoot under the moon to know the field
Through the soles of my feet to hear
The myriad leaf lives green and singing
The million million cycles of being in wing

That — before the field become solely map memory
In some archive of some architect's screen
I might possess it or it possess me
Through its night dew, its moon white caul
Its slick and shine and its profligacy
In every wingbeat in every beat of time

Paula Meehan

    The field of the poem is right next to Pobailscoil Néasain,
                       Baldoyle.

At Dublin Zoo

A four year old
Seeing an elephant
For the first time

"But it isn't blue"

Paula Meehan

(For those of us who find the festive season tough going)

Christmas

CHRISTMAS stalks me

Waits for me at corners
Sneaks up, pushes me

Reminds me
Shows me

Asks me to…

I go through the motions

Pull on ropes familiar

Listen for angels.

Then, no snow falls

No obvious crescendo

A moment, sliver of truth
Pot of hyacinths left
On my doorstep

A neighbour's child, new from last year
Blond, bonny

All heaviness leaves

This is the coming of Christ, after all

In the midst of us, again.

Anne Colgan
(December 2003)

Alannah

Some little people are very small,
Hardly there at all at all,
Purple bobbin and whale spout plume,
Who fills the space in an empty room.

Eddie Phillips

What is my name?

Your name is the goodness you're known for.
Your name is the light you throw on things.
Your name is the comfort you give by your presence.
Your name is the thing that's worth getting to know you to
find out.

Eddie Phillips

Grass Cutting

The flinty light of a false spring day
Returns us to our March duty;
Cutting the grass in my respectable
Patch of Edwardian green.
The suburban sounds of other mowers
Are thrown over make believe fences
To be composted by the wind.

Winter is shorn from the damp earth
Leaving the delicate yellow shoots
To green again between dandelion and daisy;
The shredded grass flecks my boots.
Earth and herb smells are released
To lassoe the mind back to childhood games
In the coltsfoot of youth when grey adults
Cut grass and muttered at our joy.

Now I rake the winter's mane
And scour the moss with probing tines;
Killing one form of life to enhance
The banality of bent and creeping fescue.
Meanwhile the last bloom dies on the amaryllis
Behind the window pane;
A butterfly out of season.
Another year begins.

John Walsh

Counting the Beads

We said the rosary in the evening
Kneeling, huddled on sugan chairs.
Mother sitting at a kitchen table
Her eyes a cornflower blue.

Beads knotted on swollen fingers
Limbs twisted like bare branches.
She loved when neighbours called
Sharing a pinch of snuff and gossip.

After supper she led the prayers.
The droned responses washed over us
Like gentle waves, until Granddad lost his way.
Suppressed laughter spluttered and gathered pace

But mother called a halt, a mention of lost grace.
We said the rosary at her wake,
Her limbs unfolded now and straight
Laid out on a white counterpane.

Paddy Glavin

Curled Cat

I was lying among last year's leaves
Doing nothing
Existing
Like the curled cat
At home in camouflage

All my sweeping raking and tidying
Reflexes
Are in abeyance
As nature's demolition men
Carry on around me

I am the curled cat
Idle and still
Amid flux and leaves
The inessential note
In the symphony of motion

Máiríde Woods

Lazy Poem

I should have been born a tree sloth
to swing dangling in the sun
with a green tasty wind lifting the leaves
over speckled dappled ground.

The jungle is steamy and comforting
and every branch bristles with lunch;
the river is slow as a pond
and I curl my tail delicately round
my green and supple branch.

My light heartbeat pumps like a slow tapping rain
urging growth to swell buds — pale green
they teem with possibilities...
Coloured buds soften and burst all about me.
Insects climb, birds call, animals dart through the leaves.
About me this music, abundant, and I am
a living note of its symphony
that can hear song. Oh yes.

Oh wonder — if I were a tree sloth
I could understand how little I am
and how sweetly world tastes, colours, and sings.

After I scamper around there is peace;
I must always come back to my branch
to be always an embryo suspended —
absorbing, and quietly, oh so quietly
simply living, with eyes open wide
softly breathing my peaceful 'yes'.

Sue Brown

Finglas East Journey

Slow through narrow streets
from top of 19A bus
all the coloured jumpers
waving in the playground
makes me content awhile.

Boys' play is never underhand
weird as they try to thrill.

Then along to Glasnevin
oh so many graves,
sometimes we forget funerals
but on some Sundays
with flowers as companions
you relive moments
with such a sweet will.

John O'Malley

The Foulkesmill Mill

At Foulkesmill Mill, relentlessly
The big oak mill wheel turned
Up and up the swift waters churned
Sweet music to the miller's ears

For fifty years John Murphy toiled
For fifty years the mill wheel moiled
Grinding corn every day
On the Sabbath John stayed away

Through red half door, I looked inside
He said 'come in', 'I will' I cried
He showed me round
Heart filled with pride.

Wheel black with age
He old as sage
Nigh four score years
He did not seem

From grinding corn giant mill wheels worn
Each piece and spoke
Hewn from giant Oak.
To fall between
Would crush life's dream

With eyes of child
I watched and sighed
My attention glued.
To his every move

Five well-worn floors
Four well-worn stairs
Corn this floor
Corn on that floor
Wheels a sighing
Wheels a grinding

John greased the wheels
John greased the shafts
John greased the cogs
While the mill-wheels throbbed

To lift a sack to the very top
John pulled a chord
Then through the floor
A sack did pop
And at my feet
A sack did drop

For fifty years
John worked the mill
Could lift light sacks
Upon his back
But now the sacks
Seem heavy packs.

Dust is here
Dust is there
Corn smelling dust
Is everywhere
John Murphy's lungs
It does not spare.

Dust in his eyes
Dust on his hands
Dust on the ceilings
Dust like sand

John's voice is weak
His frame is sleek
His way is gentle
Cap held high on temple

At one o'clock
John stopped the mill
A daily drill
His food was hot
But bade me stay
For the rest of day

Who'll run the mill?
When John's eyes grow dim
Will the world go on?
Without John's Mill?

John Haughton

Breakfast in Sarajevo

The bullet left the gun and made its way to its prey
Although half a mile away it did not take long
Then all life was gone for good,
Fell face first into the dirt — hurt not a bit;
Tough shit being in the wrong spot.
Caught in the sight- shot without thought
Having just bought bread for breakfast;
Now dead with his bag still in his hand
In no man's land — he was a legitimate target.
The coffee grew cold waiting for his return;
He'd lie till nightfall, before being dragged home
Though a year on the cobblestone would show his blood
A mark of where he stood when his heart stopped dead,
The sniper sipped sweet tea and sung a prayer;
While somewhere else a son went without bread
But instead his head would soon fill with a meal
Best served cold once he got older.

Ken Bryan

SKIP TO MALOO *Frances Glavin*

"You have no stick Miss" announced Johnny Murphy.

This remark came on the second day of my employment as temporary principal of a two teacher school in the foothills of North Kilkenny.

"I don't need a stick Johnny" I rejoined.

"Every teacher has one Miss", he replied.

"Well go out so and cut me a sally rod".

He arrived back with a light rod which I placed on my desk, vowing that I would never use it.

The morning flew by. I had the entire school under my command. This meant seven classes plus infants. The latter played with plasticine but I had to keep four classes studying while I initiated the remainder in the 3R's.

Lunchtime came and I was gratefully tucking into my sandwich when two very indignant little girls arrived at my desk.

"Johnny Murphy is pissing in the girl's lavatory Miss" they said.

"Send in Johnny to me".

A cheeky Johnny duly arrived.

"I believe that you have been very bold out there. Hold out your hand".

I administered three light strokes which were received with a grin.

I was a real teacher at last.

There was a harmonium parked by the wall which invited my attention.

"What about singing classes", I enquired?

"Yes miss we can sing 'Skip to Maloo'.

"Off you go then".

The singing hit the ceiling. I mentioned the harmonium, but I was told that it was inclined to fall when moved from the wall.

"Well maybe two of you could hold it up one at either end".

Six hands shot into the air and soon the instrument was shown to be in working condition. After "Skip to Maloo" I played a number of songs: The West Awake, Kelly the Boy from Killane et al. When ever pupils and teacher got frazzled we had singing which put back a smile on all our faces.

There was only one pupil in seventh class and his Arithmetic was my nightmare. The sums were all about water running out of the bath or one train passing another and similar conundrums.

"I can't do this sum Miss".

"Right Michael I'll show you when I'm finished doing the roll book".

I then spent a good ten minutes working out the sum. I sought help from my father at the weekend and I had no further problems with Arithmetic.

First Communion time came round. I was told to prepare the children. We trooped into the church for a practice run of first confession. I sat in the middle of the confession box but I left the curtain apart a little so as not to scare my young charges. I made up the sins to be confessed: I didn't say my prayers night and morning, I told lies etc. I'd love to know what they confessed to the priest when they went for real. Probably my made up sins.

I look back on that time with affection and I used the experience to my advantage in a promotion interview further down the road. I think I would have liked to be a Primary teacher but my father's strong opposition at the time to that career put it out of the question.

The Morning After The Night Before

Jetskis blasting the dawn to smithereens,
oil on the fenders, rope around the prop,
plastic and beer cans in the harbour chop.

Somebody down below is burning toast,
there's vomit in the cockpit, slick and white;
my shoes are wet, left out on deck all night.

Three shadows on the dock are looking down:
Hey listen, Mac, are these guys here with you?
A thumb jabs at my handcuffed, straggling crew.

Theo Dorgan

A Veritable Odysseus, a Classic

Menorca's principal port would lift your heart,
such handsome craft at anchor there; we lay apart,
conscious of rust, gale damage, tattered sails.

A dapper figure leaned on a varnished rail
and hailed us; we rowed across to where he stood,
upright as Nelson under a white canvas hood.

We clambered aboard, he poured a round of drinks
with a brisk flourish, saluted us with courtesy:
"All in the same boat, keeping our heads above water, eh?"

Theo Dorgan

In Tandem

She's getting her father's carpentry skills in her cooking.
She checks out grain or essence like careful measuring.
You encounter a local who enquires after the pine nuts,
You say it all joined to make a perfect entity.
Functionality comes first but the eye and the feel
Have booked their input
Before apron is donned
Or sleeves rolled up.

Eddie Phillips

Highland Games Dancer

She is close to cry in her dance to try.
Her face is the heroine's, warrior grim.
Her dance is the tale, defend, prevail.
She is grace and heart astir: a stag
atop a peak is the kilted piper trim.

But when she dances for joy and delight
we delight and rejoice in her freedom.

Eddie Phillips

Lake Bottom in Suburbia

The marl clay
Of the lake bottom
Was, I found,
No good for vegetables
But it was the only clay
In my mortgaged plot.
A hay barn overlooked my garden
When I moved in
Just thirty years ago.
Its rusty roof sang in the salty wind.
It was the last link
With the farmland of Kilbarrack.
Our arrival was more
Than it could stand.
The following year
It was replaced by a house
Which is a replica of mine.
This is how they buried
The marl clay
Of the lake bottom in Suburbia.

John Walsh

Howth Harbour

Out from the west pier two heads show.
Light reflects a sheen from bodies
half-in, half-out of the water.
Closer now dark eyes plead
mouths open to swallow handouts
from Peter on the quay.
Seagulls swoop and snatch
salt kisses in the air,
shrieks bouncing off roofs,
the sea stirring in a breeze
carries a bull-seal's cry.
Two heads rise in the water now
while we watch from the pier
one seal, then the next,
then nothing at all.

Paddy Glavin

Time of Spices

Nutmeg, ginger and cinnamon on the table again
Late November is the time of spices.
Ground almonds, raisins and sultanas
Mark days of gathering and preparation
— John went into the desert —
Behind me stand my mother and grandmother,
Those distaff generations with their wooden spoons.

Porter and rum shore up the old certainties
My bubbling kitchen bathes in pungent steam
Distilling reminiscences — his mother did things differently.
Cluttered by these our overflowing stores
We make our way through tinselly December
To the bare cave at Bethlehem. That scent of pine
And frankincense… Can this be Christmas?

Máiríde Woods

A Word About Dogs

My father's faithful dog died
in a heap in front of a car
but the man carried him to the door
and apologised, heartbroken. It was Christmas Eve.

My brother's huge dog leapt into his arms
when he came home from college
after a few months. It was autumn's rich October.

My friend's collie was rescued from the sea.
Her son, a hill walker, dove in and swam
to pull her out, untied her bonds,
and brought her home. Together
they rove the green hills in all seasons.

Our family dog devotedly guards
whoever feels down at night
and then wakes them in the morning
with a gentle nudge. It is stilly late summer.

And our young dog Bob watches us all with love
and gives his heart, true to himself,
loving and free. Pure gift.
Summer surges toward a harvest.

All dogs silently urge:
  I live.
  Love me.
  Never leave me.
  Love life.

Tenderly older angels see
us with our guardians
who nudge us back to simple loving.

Sue Brown

Windows

I thought I should see something
Up in the sky. Part of a cloud?
It's not good to say why.

For years thus the blue
Made me wonder. I was shy.

And hearing of people who dared
Icarus or poor sad Joyce
I looked on and cared.

Skies are always children —
Fleeting, better than school.
Be good, learn from us fools.

John O 'Malley

Mountain Cradle

To-day half way to the mountain peak
I lie earth cradled
A tree trunk for my pillow
The wind for my song
Ferns a-dancing
Clouds a-racing
Sun-kissed
Warming me
Rock solid

I grasp
The moment's wonderment
The bleat of lambs
Mountain peaks
Of varied hue
Blue sky mantled
Nature's canopy
Red on green
Green on green
Then let this valley
Cradle me

John Haughton

Little Friends

Let this be a lesson to you,
Stay there till I get home from work
Beneath those creaking stairs
Where light came through the cracks
That lit and split the blackness of the place.
I a child still not yet eight
Faced once more an endless wait,
Finding friends with little creatures
That crawled across my hands
And came down from above.
I grew to love these creepy-crawlies;
They like me were small and had no say,
Easily crushed and brushed aside
They'd hide in darkness to survive.
The clock ticked on outside my cell
So much so I grew to tell the time
That father's footsteps fell outside the door.
Then saying once more goodbye
To spiders and other tiny friends
I stood up to face the music
Of the voice above my head.
Come out it said and don't do that again;
That's the way life would be from then on in,
Punished for being born and getting in the way,

Ken Bryan

THE CUT OF MY JIB *Frances Glavin*

It must be something about the shape of my face or the cut of my jib because I often find myself chatting to total strangers. Recently when I was leafing through a magazine in a dentist's waiting room a fellow patient drew my attention to a picture in a magazine of some very large ladies tucking into enormous helpings of cakes and buns. She informed me that her son "He's a doctor, you know", had refused a large helping of cabbage which she had set in front of him when he came on a visit. He told her it would distend his stomach, and that he would be able to eat a lot more and eventually become a habitual overeater. I didn't believe much of her story and formed the opinion that he must be a "Spin Doctor" spinning yarns! The encounter was as sensible as the meeting on the train with a lady who announced that
"They would have to do something about dogs in the budget".

On another occasion I was standing at a bus stop trying to put spells on Dublin Bus! What a waste of witchcraft! There was another lady in the queue. I smiled at her and we discussed the transport situation. A car drew up and a lady offered us a lift. Gratefully, we accepted and discovered another occupant in the car - a huge shaggy dog.

The car's owner was a dog lover and she had been down on Dollymount Strand airing herself and her canine friend. Quite suddenly she braked and peered across the road at a little white terrier
"Oh that's not the dog I'm looking for", she said
"There's a stray around here I'm trying to find and bring to the "Dog's Home".
Her manner was eccentric but I relaxed when I realised she was a very good driver.

She must have brought out the worst in me because I asked how she coped with any odd characters whom she encountered on Dollymount Strand.
"Oh the dirty devils", she said.

"Ye have no idea of the queers I meet".

"Them oul fellas are the worst but I'm well able for them with my walking stick".

I had a fleeting vision of a number of citizens stumbling round the sand dunes clutching their bleeding heads, their bad intentions long forgotten. A doggy smell permeated the car and the covered seats looked as if they were woven with dog's hair. I glanced at my fellow passenger. Her eyes were wide with fright. Her mother had probably told her not to take lifts from strange men, but had forgotten to mention strange women!

I announced that I was near home and thanked the driver for the lift. As I was leaving the car the other woman's eyes seem to say,

"How can you leave me with this strange person"?

I giggled as I put my key in the front door. I thought of what a woman I met at a funeral had said,

"People does be very drear these days. You'd need an aul laugh to keep you going".

My most unusual encounter was in a coffee shop in Grafton Street. Seated next to me was a distinguished looking middle-aged man. He asked me to pass the sugar and we started to talk. His North American accent fascinated me and he told me he was a Canadian University Professor on a year's sabbatical on his way to Paris via Dublin. It so happened that I was planning a visit to his hometown, Montreal, in the autumn. When he heard this he unloaded his worries. His daughter Catherine had visited Ireland the previous summer, fallen madly in love with an Irishman and was planning to return to marry him. Her family did not think a holiday romance was a good basis for a permanent relationship.

After some discussion I promised to phone her when I got to Montreal and impress on her that Irishmen were full of blarney and to think hard before she made any firm decisions!

In the autumn I met Catherine in downtown Montreal. I must have made a rotten job of exposing the treachery of Irishmen because she phoned me from Kinsale the following year, and was I gathered, merrily playing the field. I haven't had sound or sight of her since. Perhaps she took a lift from a strange woman!

Patrick the Herdsman

Patrick was a pig man.
He knew the run of swine.
Their whine and squeal and shriek
Were all plain chant to him.
Coming back to Hibernia,
He remembered his old trade.
He played a trick or two
To silence the tirade,
To shock and awe the herd.

The people watched him
Through their rain-sodden locks.
Their eyes cautious but hungry.
Here was a herd ripe for turning
To face new fires
And learn new fears.
Snake-like he garnered them.
Mesmerising their souls.
He penned them with his crook
And fed them shamrock
From his hand.

John Walsh

Wings

While sowing seed potatoes,
from nowhere a splash of redbreast
flew into my ken
into my ken.

Tiny eyes viewed smallholdings
enfolding withered stalks
where ancestors scrabbled
in the grey light *within, within.*

Dig deep, the eyes semaphored.
For a moment our two worlds touched
when the robin crossed a line
at my feet, *at my feet.*

His waistcoat was the colour
of grandfather's apron
that he wore while shaping wood,
shaping wood.

A builder with keen eyes,
and so had the robin
as he devoured a beetle
hiding in the earth, *hiding in the earth.*

They both brought magic
from trees as ancient as the hills,
to earth, flower and wood
Earth, flower and wood.

Stay awhile' I whispered
in this garden of dreams.
But robin and grandfather
flew out of my ken, *out of my ken.*

Paddy Glavin

A Sense of Time

The hearth-fire burning
The tick-tock of clock
The clip-clop hooves
The flickering candle
Embers fading
All these and
A sense of time
Are now no more

John Haughton

Inquest

Blank page no more
Frozen as significant

Half hour before.
Say something, anything,
Break the silence,
Prepare to walk Balscadden,
Where, as far as we know he went in.

By coincidence Conor
Has a map on the floor.

One of those dull days
Looking at depths
Distances from the shore saying
'Where will we be this summer
this autumn?

Hearing the hurt again.
His body described,
The anguish is complete.

I'm in a lonely Coroner's Court
Way out in Swords.
The time it took, scarcely
Twenty full minutes.
His decision maybe seconds
Never to be forgotten
Those wonderful months
In part preparing
To meet the world.
Not this one,
The next.

John O 'Malley

Marathon Man

Marathon man has no shape
All sizes pilgrim-like
Wend their way
Like river meander
Like sheep winding mountain

At starting horn
unleashed
The urge forward
Is quickly quelled

A hush of expectancy
Disciplined throng
Camaraderie born
Like brother to brother

Winners all
Spina bifida
Children's Leukemia
Conquer cancer
Muscular dystrophy

Giving of all
The better side of man
Good will like oxen harnessed
Unflinchingly to the goal

The noble savage
Tamed at last
His better side revealed
Success or failure
Equally rewarded

Then battered bodies
Battle worn
Struggle on
Some fall or falter
Body mind contorted

Birth pang's pain
Life's mysteries
From streets of desolation and elation
Beauty's born

John Haughton

Fourteen Summers

At the age of ten plus two.
They said sign on son you'll do.
With your five foot three or more
You're just what we're looking for.
With your brown eyes clear and bright.
Three and nine will set you right.
More than you have ever seen,
Serving kingdom, king and queen.

At the age of ten plus three.
What a sight you were to see.
With your uniform and gun.
Who'd have thought you were so young.
Drilling till you got it right.
Taught you how to march and fight.
Yet you looked the proper gent.
In your Royal Irish Regiment

At the age of ten plus four.
Found you on the Belgium shore.
With the scream of shot and shell.
Oh it must have seemed like hell.
You a child and yet a man.
Doing the best a body can.
As the fight for Ypres raged on.
There you died my poor wee John.

Now in Belgium's soil you lie.
You the youngest boy to die.
From the Irish shore you came.
Johnny Condon was your name.
Just a boy of fourteen years.
It would make a stone cry tears.
All who pass along this way.
Say a prayer for John today

Fourteen summers are not long
Fourteen winters were soon gone.
Fourteen autumns far too few.
Fourteen springtimes flew by you.
Oh young love never stood a chance.
When death swept you up to dance.
You a child who never knew.
What a lassie's kiss could do

Ken Bryan

Touchdown

Bay, open bay, spread out below
the cloud banks, cloud–dappled, drenched
in greens and greys, scarred
by the gradual and the sudden
in equal parts, but firm;

one foot-sized expanse of it,
and beside it another, that waits glistening
for the relaxing of muscle, of tendon, the folding
of wing and reach, the dip
and careful drift into touchdown, into the sodden

solidity of place — screech
of other selves, echoing of hunger
and exhaustion, and ache, sheer, collective ache,
after so much longing, so much of nothing
else to depend on, after so much air.

Pat Boran

SQUARE BASHING *Paddy Glavin*

On a Friday morning the platoon all brassoed, blancoed and boot polished were on the square an hour before the officers arrived. Private Bartley late again was still polishing his brasses while running down the stairs. He slid into position before the brigade commanders known to the rank and file as "The Brass Hats" mounted a platform to view the drill display. A three star general surrounded by subalterns sat in the centre. For weeks past the company sergeant had trained the platoon in drill formations. They had marched weaving intricate patterns on the square, clutching rifles for hours every day. At times their studded brown boots generated sparks in response to the sergeant's tongue. The general had ordered that today the commands be given in Irish. Peter saw worry in the platoon commander's eyes. Lieutenant Brown informed them that he would mouth and mime the orders before shouting out the actual commands in the native tongue.

Sunlight glistened on buttons and rifles. The platoon standing at ease waited. At last the Lieutenant's lips moved. He's like a ventriloquist Peter thought.

" Cara", the young officer shouted.

What the hells going on Peter wondered, surely he means "Aire"? At last the platoon responded and waited at attention for a translation of "Quick March".

The Lieutenant's lips moved as perspiration fell from his forehead. Worry showed in his eyes. Peter felt sorry for him. At last the platoon picked up the command "Mairseal". They marched off in step arms swinging in unison moving briskly across the square. In the distance a high brick wall loomed. All ears were waiting for the next order. Their boots sang out 'Left- Right, Left-Right, but no order came.

Like a breeze in a barley field a ripple of suppressed laughter caressed the platoon. It was a reaction to the constant hectoring on the barrack square. A spark of resistance emerged. How could they obey if no order came? They weren't robots now. In thirty seconds the platoon will crash into the wall. It will end in a shambles Peter thought.

He heard himself saying aloud "Thart Iompaigh" a yard from the wall. The platoon turned as one. With perfect timing Peter had saved the display.

Prayer for the Ship of State

Too many paving stones
Have been caulked
With blood of children
To let us sing
A Soldier's Song.
Too many faces
Have been furled in anguish
To let us
Salute a flag.
Let us draw the flags from the mast
And let silence be our air.
Let us set sail again
Without banner, without anthem.
For ballast
Clean stones will suffice.

John Walsh

For Dad, During the McCarthy Hearings

'Somewhere on earth there is a peaceful place for peaceable
men...'
Isaac Walton

'They will arrest us,' he said, his wise kind eyes
brown with living fleck of sun, as lifeful
as a pond in summer.
We tried to hope, in the gravelled yard.
And then the trucks came, closed cartons of steel
and men with hard faces and closed-inside eyes.
Wagons into wasteland, pillars of ugliness.
Is this a wasteheap of human lives not lived yet?

We are separated, and the questions come,
like mortars that rip my body parts away.
I must not reveal, I must not reveal
O let darkness come, then I cannot reveal
anything that can be turned on him
or anyone he or I loves.

I will live; the wise white-robed Child
Whose features, like a lamplight of safety,
drew me in — that Child comes — but when
I say that, I meet contempt, bright-brittle,
which rattles my teeth and my bones.

I will wait for the Child to come again
and bring me to some place
where love shelters and warms like hearth fire
even though the tall dark green pines
burn in a wild white sweep of snow.

Sue Brown

The Dark Horseman

Hoofbeats behind me again…
Even on the sunlit motorway the shadow
Of that dark horseman.
But I will not swing round
And meet the cold eye I turned from
Thirty years ago, the one that made
Pillars of salt of so many.

At the wheel on the highway
I know how far I've come…
Friends and relatives,
Laughter and candles hold back the dark…
Yet on the odd, unpopulated evening
The breath that tickles my neck
Is terribly familiar.

Mostly I mock my horseman. In this day and age…
High cliffs, and the temptation
Of nothingness are years away.
Surely if he existed
He would drive a BMW
Not canter softly in my wake
Like some desultory traveller.

Yet there is no surety…
Abysses open at every junction,
Loved ones vanish
Even in my embrace. From the TV
Foreign horrors beckon,
Yet all these workaday years
I have clung on grimly.

But the nights grow darker after Samhain
Tasks trickle away, acquaintances
Take their leave. Bach and Mozart
Whisper thinly against the silence
My strength is spent, I fooster
With particles of dust, awaiting
The show-down with my dark follower.

Máiríde Woods

Goodnight

Can there be a secret
Sunset after hours?
Try letting passion out...

We cannot speak for others
More's our luck.

Getting by, there's a fluke.
But the universe
Has to be gained,
Our idea of it
Partially feigned.

We would meet each
Other, on a matter
Not known.

Francis Holmes will hereafter
Be a martyr
He left his hurling stick at home.

Regard the moon
In the little time that's left
And it's shadows
Shred in wounds

Who is it that follows after
Singing as she comes,
Allow her present laughter
She has many chums.

John O 'Malley

Rainforests

Rainforests life giving
Support systems
Round the belly of the globe
God's gift to man.

Yet man hacks blindly
At life supporting system
With death wish of self-destruct.

Think globally! Act locally!
Plant, preserve, conserve
Harvest prudently
The forests of the world.

Trees for shelter
Trees for oxygen
Trees for medicine
Trees for beauty
Trees for food
Trees for clean air
Trees for crafts
Trees for furniture
Trees to screen
Trees to build
Trees for people
People for trees

Man and trees
Part of life's web
Sharing species-rich
Habitats of mother earth
In diversity.

John Haughton

Katanga Dawn

In the land to The River which swallows all Rivers,
dawn is brief to swiftly fire the mists of night.
Startling their appearance then, at cusp of day,
as dark goddesses transient through our time.
As from a dream. Statuesque,
attired in sapphire, gilt and crimsons. The trio
call in unison tradition's greeting, *Jambo!*
Then *Habari* found response-*mzuri kapisa,*
and a smile presaging sun. Not deities,
but earthly women these, of simple grace.
A moment there, as quickly gone.
Burdened for a marketplace
by pathways through this rainy-season bush.
Left behind
the gracious words, engaging smiles,
a memory of multi-coloured cloths.
Most of all, awareness of the soul of Africa.

Séamus ua Trodd

In Memory Of My Mother

I see you clearly in the kitchen in Drumcondra
Baking the hot brown bread and standing
Over the cooker watching the rich and
Steamy steak and kidney pie coming to the boil.

Bringing me by the hand to early morning
Mass at the convent of St. Alphonsus,
Where the nuns tutored me in latin and later I became
An altar boy — closer to God and closer to your love and
affection.

Walking across the fields of St. Anne's Park
To Monday night devotions in St.Brigid's, but above all,
listening to your voice as you entertained around the piano
at home Of a Sunday evening: Where are all the singers now?

Your voice vibrant with Joy and laughter
As you brought a life so brimming and full
To all who visited: Joy was all around.

Your presence has never left me — especially
When I sat still in my quiet, sacred place,
On the cliff walk in Howth —
Soon after you passed on.

Then I was void with grief,
My life was fragmented,
like the broken stained-glass window
In the nearby St.Fintan's church,

I learned that it's never too late to shed a tear.
But this is not a place of tears.
Alone as I gazed across Dublin Bay,
Among the wild myrtle and red heather

I watched the sky meeting the distant horizon at the summit
I turned around and walked away,
With the strains of your songs,
Echoing in my ears.

Joe Fitzpatrick

TELEGRAMS *Máiríde Woods*

My mother taught me to write telegrams — not that I now use that spare and terrible craft. She thought she was setting me up with a useful skill and in a way she was right. Telegrams were charged by the word so succinctness made good business sense. For my mother the terseness of the telegram was part of that frugal world she came from.

Telegrams spelt death and illness- they came on yellow paper with curious black divisions so they had something of the look of the In Memoriam card. I remember one day on the way home from school my mother met us, the thin piece of paper in her hand, telling her that her favourite uncle was dead. We understood death no more than telegrams but we felt their fatefulness - the way they allowed distant ills to overshadow the everyday pain of losing one's best friend.

In those days we would put our ears against telegraph poles and imagine the words flowing along the wires to our granny in Dublin. There were disembodied voices in the wires just as there were guardian angels beside us. The telegraph evoked poetic flights of fancy when first introduced and was a far more marvellous leap forward than the mobile phone. In 1844 the Exeter reporter wrote: "professor Morse's Electro Magnetic ... is not merely a beautiful illustration of a philosophical principle, but an agent that may be made of practical and every day utility..."

My mother's telegrams were composed in the post office under the stern eye of the postmistress with the dial-up telephone rather than Samuel Morse as transmitter. And although the postmistress was a benign figure, it was important to phrase your missive so as to give as little as possible away to the uninstructed reader. In the fifties secrecy was a way of life although we had little to be secretive about. I spent hours devising codes for my diary (secret of course) in which I wrote with great difficulty about the weather and our meagre comings and goings.

My parents also had a collection of wedding telegrams which we delighted in reading — mainly from people that we didn't know but who took on a separate and fantastical life from their scribbled congratulations. Cousins and friends — some already vanished.

Later when my parents were both dead, I found another set of telegrams I had never seen. Stuck into the cover of an album. Sent in the January days around my birth from my aunt to my father. The delivery wards of those days had no room for fathers, there was no such thing as paternity leave. My mother had come back to her parents' house in Dublin before my birth; while my father had returned to his teaching job in Wales.

The first telegram, dated 10 pm on the 18th, said baldly that my mother had gone into the nursing home at 9; the second dated the next morning simply said; No news yet; the third: Still no news; the fourth, dated midnight the following night, Mary Ita arrived 10 pm, Deo Gratias. It would be five weeks before my father actually saw me.

I feel for my mother, of course, having given birth myself. But more often I think of my father, reading those telegrams in the small town digs to which he had returned in my mother's absence; coming back from his very English public school, drinking the still rationed tea with the old couple who later made me a doll's cradle, sitting by their fire in the post-war cold, out of his country. Childbirth was riskier then and he was a worrier. "Always sit towards the back of the plane", he would warn me later, his worst-case strategy to hand. I can only imagine how anxious he was as he sat watching the gate, waiting and dreading the sound of the telegraph boy's bicycle bell. In such circumstances it's not possible to be soothed. People were more religious in those days; I suppose he prayed, or bargained with God, the way I would have.

When I look at those telegrams I thank God for the telephone, for the way that news, bad or good, now comes in a human voice, one you can reply to and argue with, not in someone else's dead handwriting on yellow paper.

Súgáins

For haymaking we needed súgáins.
My father collected a forkful
Of smooth grass from the sward.
He picked a stick from the hedge
And placed it in my hands.
"Start twisting" he said.
Then he looped the hay around the stick
And as I reversed still twisting.
A snake of ropey hay
Formed between my father's hands;
Magic in a meadow
In the bright light of day.
When long enough to sag,
Each súgáin was rolled into a ball.
They nestled in the headland
Like dinosaur eggs until evening time.
We used them to tie down each wynd.
Then the darkness gathered
In the corners of the dew-damp field
And the corncrake cleared his throat
For an evening recital.
The miracle of a hay rope
Binds me to the memory.

John Walsh

Old Photographs

Old Photographs — withered now,
lie scattered, abandoned.
Found in a suitcase by a
mischievious child.
Fading confetti once thrown
on a couple,
together — united by their hopes
and dreams.
To share in life's laughter,
the hardship, the tears,
to sit up with sick children,
to kiss away fears.

No need for the late nights,
the traipsing of stairs,
no more Christmas morning
wigs or sleepy eyes — but
to turn now full circle —
on this twenty-three year ride,
to finish together – with no sticky fingers
to clean — to know that together
the love will be seen,
old photographs abandoned
by unknowing eyes but to you
our dear parents — a memory
strong and in this poem a
gift of remembrance of a day that is gone.

Caitríona Geraghty

Take these chains from my heart ...

Those corny blood and chain images
Leave rust marks on my page.
The crimson hearts, sharp swords and arrows,
Escape from my school-books; science, history and religion
Swirling together. Auricles hum
To ventricles, sin waltzes with redemption.
The Sacred Heart bares his long-running sorrow
From our vanished mantelpiece, forty year old wrecks
Groan beside Carnlough quay.

It's all in the mind, I tell myself,
Remembering brains like hermit crabs
Or shrivelled walnuts. The heart
Is just a sealed-in organ beating interminably;
Chains make no difference, despite old Ray Charles.
The Sacred Heart looks out across my life
And hums a complicated blues. Chain music.

Máiríde Woods

Problem
(for my Dad)

I

My father was a defending lawyer who stood at the bar
and pleaded and fought for anyone who came to him,
not just in court, but toYahweh at the golden bar of heaven.
And when I asked him foolishly, 'doesn't it bother you,
defending a guilty man?' he said 'Don't you think
a guilty man needs a friend, more than an innocent
one does? He feels bad about himself, and
he will let himself be blamed too much; not only
that, but other people will say he did other things
he didn't do. He needs me more.' The only thing
that ever made him angry was someone judging
or hardening their heart. 'How dare you,'
he would storm in anguish; 'look at yourself, you are judging?
Change your life and let yourself walk in their
shoes for a month. Tell me it doesn't hurt.'

It seems so hard to be like that sometimes, but now when
life is pressing so hard, when it is family troubles time, and
I look for love in every pair of eyes I meet, and
I often see (o surprise) a stranger looking at me
with the features of a brother who is loved and full of love,
or another one (o sadness) with the eyes
of a child who is loving, full of love, but broken and confused
or (o hopeful way) another with the lean frame
of a wayfarer who just can't find
a bed for the night anywhere and yet sleeps
peacefully in straw like that in which
Jesus was lain (o mystery) as a baby.
I see His friends, and hear my father's voice.

And the Lord is a healer, and this world is His field
hospital — but sometimes only the patients are here to do
the nursing, and the physicians are doing the work
of our dear Physician's mind, thought, and hands.
This broken world seems in some startling way a gift
from the healer, so we will come to understand
how He loves us and wants us to live.
We are meant — it seems — to bring one another to
fuller aliveness, to love Him yearningly as
He has loved us, and to love one another without fear, although
perhaps in pain He wanted to protect us from.
As my Dad did and does love people, even those who hurt
him and us — like that — I will try... I try.
His heart and mind were so ready, and so without fear.

II

Whenever I am teaching a poet, it seems
it is early evening, the lamps are lit in the field hospital;
I bring meals around, and one of the tired, shadowed
hollow-eyed patients starts up a song
full of love and longing. We all clap and
are at home, a suddenly created home.
I see Him among us, standing watching, serious and kind;
The air is tinted dusky red by His love.
But He is also the voice of the young soldier singing,
and these are His Hands, His working Hands.
All this love I owe my father, the gentle rabbi
of our hearts who told a thousand stories,
and left a legacy of one command,
'Love people without anger — and live.'

Sue Brown

A Man Called Nobody

(December 1992)

He staggered across Amiens Street
In rain and sleet
Dodging cars
Full of jars

Drunk as a skunk
Way out as a punk
Nobody cared
Or to help him dared

He looked a bum
Every bit a scum
A castaway
So they say

To the eye- a lout
Another layabout
Face so gaunt
Like ghosted haunt

Battered and bruised
Full of booze
From deep bruise
His blood did ooze

Be-deviled and shakin'
His body forsaken
A soul for the takin'
Movements fakin'

The night was cold
The wind was bitter
Old Jack Frost
Was in the litter

Once a babe
His mother raved
And her sweet milk
As soft as silk

He weaved right
He weaved left
Bobbing and diving
Like old age jiving

Sleeping rough
Made him tough
And flutter flutter
In the gutter

Each night he'd sleep
Dreams not so deep
In cardboard box
No Fort Knox

He used to dance
He used to sing
For years he made
The pavements ring

He once went wild
And the crowds beguiled
Light on his feet
Like falling sleet

Deaf to car horns
Deaf to driver's scorns
To each car phone

'Póg mo hone'

Inside a soul
No one could see
Except the few
Their faith decree

Hail McVerry
And Merchants' Quay
Vincent de Paul
And Simon's Hall

Help Ethiopia
Our myopia
To have or to be
Trapped in poverty

Four lanes he crossed
Like old Jack Frost
Just one to go
He mustn't slow

He stepped out
But what a clout
A motorbike
Like sharpened spike

The sirens blared
A small crowd dared
To shield his body
From heavy lorry

Death was so kind
And in no time
It drew across
Life's earthly blind

No one to mourn
But poverty condone
Except a priest
His soul release

Greed can blind
And slowly grind
And force humanity
From love to flee

While Christmas shoppers
Fill their coffers
A pauper's grave
Beckons Dave

His journey's end
Without a friend
No more he'll roam
His soul flown home

John Haughton

White Sticks

The blind man sees no neon
lights nor traffic signals green
but walks along
stick in hand bravely to himself he keeps.

If he takes a chance to talk
the words he gives are few.
for courtesy he expects with
a Light thought the help we give.

Every other day or so
I like to see so brave a band
as carry tapping their white sticks
no verse we make can touch.

John O 'Malley

THE SKERRIES I REMEMBER *Joe Fitzpatrick*

"I remember, I remember the house where I was born." This is from one of the earliest poems that I learned at school, growing up in Skerries, north County Dublin. In the 1940's and 1950's it was very similar to growing up in a village. My Mother's maiden name was Grimley. She had two brothers who were later educated in St. Vincent's Orphanage in Dublin, because my grandmother (Brigid) was widowed early in her married life. My Grandfather, James Grimley, a sea captain, was killed at sea.

As I grew up I discovered I had relatives on nearly every street Grimes, and Duff, plus the Keane's in Strand Street, were all cousins of my family. I went to school in the Holy Faith Convent (which is now demolished). There had been a *Grand Hotel* near the monument, where I discovered my parents had their wedding reception, in 1931.

Subsequently, one of my mother's brothers, Joseph, joined the Columban Fathers, which was then known as the Maynooth Mission to China. He was ordained in Dalgan Park, Co Meath, in 1932 and he immediately set sail to begin his missionary work in china. *The Drogheda Independent* reported at the time of his ordination that: "...The Rev. Joseph Grimley was given a great reception in Skerries: arriving by motor, Father Grimley was met a mile outside the town by a large gathering of townspeople and the St.Patrick's Brass and Reed band and escorted to his home. Rockets were fired, bonfires blazed in the street and the houses were illuminated."

Fr Joe, as we affectionately knew him, became a major role model for me as a young boy growing up in Skerries. Following the Second World War, having spent 14 years on the missions, he returned home to Skerries in 1947. Much of that time was spent listening to his stories from China, and of the war, and showing us his photos taken over many years. The year 1947 was one of the coldest years ever recorded, with constant snow during the winter. Fr. Joe had the whole town making snow ploughs, and I can still see, in my mind's eye, people dragging their toboggans up the Mill Hill and the golf path, then sliding down again, to great hilarity and laughing.

The highlight of the year for me was making my First Holy Communion in the convent - indeed a very special occasion for the six of us (including the Fanning brothers and Ann Stapleton). Although I was only six years of age, I received a special dispensation because my uncle was home from the missions.

Listening to my mother Mai and my aunts, I soon gathered many stories and enjoyed listening as they shared their memories. I can still taste Mrs. Moles' lovely raspberry juice which she made in her kitchen, and Mrs. Burkes (wife of the local Garda) delicious home-made brown bread and scones lavished on us as we came home from school. The local picture house, *The Pavilion,* was always a hive of activity and the films changed every two nights. I can recall the postman collecting the white enamel cases from the station as the train brought down the films from Dublin, and then delivering them to Leo Flannagan, the proprietor of the cinema, in his pony and trap.

Leo also ran one of the most famous Dance Halls/Ballrooms in Dublin, which was also known as *The Pavilion.* It had a wonderfully wide, panoramic view of the islands that surrounded the strand street. The Ads in the papers proclaimed the readers that it was: "The most beautiful ballroom in Ireland". And it was.

Who could forget the lovely warm summers? Eamonn Quinn, father of senator Feargal Quinn, built one of the first holiday camps in the country at red island, named naturally enough, *Red Island.* Strangely, the other one, was Billy Butler's holiday camp at Mosney, Co. Meath.

Other memories flood back: making hay with my godfather John Grimes on fields near the railway station, picking raspberries and strawberries in Mr. Monk's fields near the Balbriggan Road and walking the country lanes. As a group of youngsters we seemed to walk everywhere, and our special haunt was the Old Mill Bakery owned by the Ennis family. I still remember the smell of the fresh bread being baked, wafting across the fields, with it's pungent aroma, stronger than any woman's perfume.

We swam along the clean beaches - the more advanced swimmers would swim around the Heads, which was a path around

Red Island and where The Springboards and The Captain's were located. The nuns had their own private bathing boxes at the South Strand where they could enjoy their sandwiches and undress in privacy. I recall vividly being able to walk out to She-nick Island when the tide was out, once we got there we would gaze out to Rockabill lighthouse, and St. Patrick's island nearby.

Another summer highlight was the crowds of holiday makers from Scotland (we could never understand their accents!) and England who came in their hundreds every month to stay at *Red Island.* This of course was the era before cheap flights, and holidays to the continent before it became fashionable and affordable to the masses. The visitors were forever welcome by the towns-people and many lasting friendships were struck up, and they never ceased to bring great colour and glamour to the town.

July always brought the outstanding attraction that was known as the *Skerries 100* - the motorcycle races. The 100 stood for the amount of laps that the riders rode around the roads of Milverton and Skerries. The smell of oil and petrol filled the air as the riders sped past the watching crowds. Riders came from every corner of Ireland and included such men as Reg Armstrong, William McCandless and Louis Carter. In more recent years the famous Honda 50 cc bikes appeared. The Pits were located across the road from the cemetery at Holmpatrick and was formerly a brewery.

So as I look back over the years, I see the De La Salle Brothers in the *Grand Hotel,* the dancing couples in *Red Island* and Hal Roach acting as camp entertainer; the rugby match held every August between the local 15 and the visitors from Dublin, and "Cheap" Jack selling his wares from his Morris van- everything "from a Needle to an anchor". I see the lush green fields, filled with contented cows and sheep grazing peacefully at us as we walked by along the lanes: and at night-time, the sound of Jim Bacon and his Orchestra floating across the sea from *The Pavilion.*

Biographies

Séamus ua Trodd was born mid-20th Century in Shannon Valley. He has read his work in Ireland, Great Britain and Canada. He has a new collection in preparation for publication.

Pat Boran is the author of four collections of poetry, short fiction for adults and children, and four non-fiction works including the popular writers' handbook: *The Portable Creative Writing Workshop.*

Sue Brown grew up in a rural New England town. Her father was from a Lithuanian refugee family and many Polish refugees had bought small farms in the Connecticut River valley. She came to Ireland as a student, fell in love, married and moved to Bayside. Here her son and daughter grew up and one of the aspects of Bayside she loves most is the natural and nurturing setting it provides for children. She trains primary school teachers in storytelling, sharing books with children, and creating puppets.

Ken Bryan is living in the northside of Dublin. He has been writing for the last 25 years and is influenced by other poets, namely Robert Frost and Robert Service. These are his first published poems.

Anne Colgan lives locally in Sutton Park. She has four grown up children and she has just completed a BA Hons degree in English Literature in St. Patrick's College, Drumcondra.

Thomas Delaney was born in Dublin in 1947. Originally from Patrick Street he later moved to East Wall where he worked by trade as a fitter turner up until 2002. He has published a book of poems entitled "The Poet Asks Why". He is a prolific poet and teaches Appreciation of Literature and Creative Writing in Greendale Community College. At present he is working on another collection which he intends to call *Black on White*. The proceeds of which will go to the homeless.

Theo Dorgan is a poet, broadcaster, editor and documentary scriptwriter. His most recent books are *Sailing for Home*, a personal account of a transatlantic journey under sail, and *Songs of Earth and Light*, translations of the Slovenian poet Barbara Korun.

Joe Fitzpatrick larger than life character sadly passed from our midst shortly after he had prepared his script for our new book. To his sorrowing wife Pauline and sons, Fr.Victor, Jason and David, our deepest sympathy.

Caitríona Geraghty was born in Sutton Park in 1969. Educated at Pobalscoil Neasáin, Scoil Chaitríona and N.U.I.G. She has worked in radio, PR and is now in community development work in Fingal County Council.

Frances Glavin was born in North Kilkenny. She wrote in secondary school and was in *Klear* in the eighties. Frances work appeared in two Klear publications and in Trinity's Writer's Group last two books: *The Jericho Road* and *Concetti 2000*.

Paddy Glavin was born and reared in Listowel and came to Dublin in the mid-fifties. He became a teacher in 1970. He married Frances and they settled in Bayside in 1974, where they still live. After retiring he took up writing poems and stories.

John Haughton is author of, 'The Silver Lining', which is the story of Lady Heath and the history of Irish aviation in the 1930s. He was editor of two anthologies of poems about the environment, written by pupils of the Ballyfermot schools, under the title, *'The Forest of Children Dreaming'*. This formed part of 'The Ballyfermot Schools Forest Project' an innovative environmental project. John was co-editor of the Forest Friends Ireland/Cáirde na Coille anthology of poetry, *'Seeing the Wood and the Trees'*. Some of his poems are included in the Trinity Writer Group's publication, *'Trinity Collage'*.

Daniel Kelly was born in Dublin. After school he travelled to

Germany where he lived and worked for a year. After settling back at home for a few years he packed his bags and headed to Vienna. This adventure filled his life with a new found wonder and romanticism. Although writing for many years this is his first work to be published.

Cathal Melinn is another native writer to the collection. He lived and worked in Vienna for a few years. He worked as an editor for Yahoo and also trained as a copy writer in advertising. He likes writing childrens stories.

Paula Meehan has published five collections of poetry, the more recent being *Dharmakaya* from Carcanet Press. She has also written plays for both adults and children. Her play *Threehander* won an award for best Radio Drama of 2005.

John O'Malley grew up in East Limerick. After working in London in the early sixties he returned to Dublin where exposure to the arts and friendships made him develop a love for poetry. He has lived in Bayside since 1970 and is now retired, where he is writing more than ever.

Eddie Phillips winged his way from West Wicklow in the early 60s. (He says, 'thank you Dublin for having me.') He found Anne, a Dublin girl, and they've nested in Bayside for nearly thirty years. Always a word fan Eddie, it took the Trinity Writers' Group of Donaghmede Library to get him going with the quill. Along with the attendant reading that goes with writing he feels he's only in the early foothills of a Rockies adventure.

Emmet Vincent is 24 years old and likes to write short stories, watch movies, listen to music, read books by Kurt Vonnegut and John Irving and engage in any other activity that involves very little exercise. One day he hopes to write a novel. He hasn't yet decided on the subject matter but the protagonist will definitely wear some sort of knitted jumper. His ambition is to find some-one who will pay him currency for the material he writes but as of yet he hasn't discovered anybody with a low enough IQ who is willing to do this.

John Walsh was born in Kilmallock, Co. Limerick and grew up watching small towns die while horses were replaced by tractors. Early influences were *The Limerick Leader* and the BBC on long-wave. Being close to life and nature and death provided the stimulus for early writings. Urban angst has added to that inspiration. He has been seeking asylum in the public service for the last thirty years.

Paul Wickham was born in Clontarf, reared in Howth, a frequent visitor to friends in Bayside and Kilbarrack over the years, in pursuit of genuine Christian Community. Having studied and worked at pharmacy he is now working as a general nurse for care of elderly people. Music, song and word play are his great loves.

Máiríde Woods was born in Dublin but spent her childhood in Cushendall, Co Antrim. She writes poetry, short stories and radio drama. She won a Hennessy Award in 1992 and several awards for RTE. Her work has appeared in many Irish Anthologies. In her other life she has worked as a teacher and researcher. She has lived with her family in Bayside for almost thirty years. Máiríde's first book *The Lost Roundness of the World* was published this year.